745·4 wh

DESIGN**TOPICS**

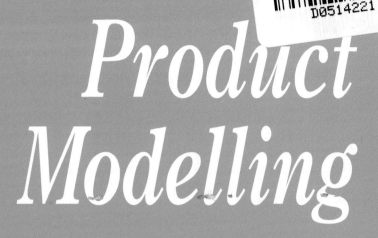

Product Modelling

Jennifer Cottis

Oxford University Press

INTRODUCTION

Industrial designers – sometimes called product designers – create the products we use. They give products their colour, texture, and personality. They design them to be safe to use and to fit well into their surroundings.

Product designers present their ideas in many different ways, depending upon the product and the stage of the design. They use drawings, models, photography, and computer-generated videos to explain and sell their ideas.

This book is about one aspect of presentation that product designers use – models.

The product modelled throughout this book is a battery-operated vacuum cleaner, but this is not an instruction manual for building one . The example of modelling this product gives general information on materials and methods, so that the principles can be applied easily to modelling other products.

Jennifer Cottis 1991

Safety note: a number of photographs on pp 33, 34 and 60 show machine tools in use without their safety guard attachment. This is for illustrative purposes of the technique only and does not constitute a recommendation of workshop practice as safety guards and goggles should be used at all times.

Oxford University Press, Walton Street, Oxford OX2 6DP

Oxford New York Toronto
Delhi Bombay Calcutta Madras Karachi
Petaling Jaya Singapore Hong Kong Tokyo
Nairobi Dar es Salaam Cape Town
Melbourne Auckland

and associated companies in
Berlin Ibadan

Oxford is a trade mark of Oxford University Press

© Jennifer Cottis

First published 1991

A CIP catalogue record for this book is available from the British Library.

ISBN 019 832761 7

Typeset in News Gothic by
Tradespools Ltd, Frome, Somerset
Printed in Singapore

Acknowledgements

Photography by **Jennifer Cottis** and **Chris Honeywell**.

Illustrations by **Jennifer Cottis**.

Oxford University Press would like to thank **Nick Rose** and **St Augustines School**, Iffley, Oxford for their kind help and assistance.

CONTENTS

Presenting ideas

Designers must be able to 'sell' their designs, and to do this they must communicate their ideas effectively. Designers need to let other people know what their designs are like. There is no point in spending a lot of time designing something if the ideas cannot be communicated well.

There are no fixed rules about how to present information. But most designers use pictorial views and flat views of their design at some stage in the design process.

Pictorial views

Pictorial views are drawings which show the appearance of the product but do not give much information about the materials or construction. **Orthographic projection** is used to show flat views of your design. These are called **plans** and **elevations**. They give more detailed information than pictorial views about dimensions and how the product will be made.

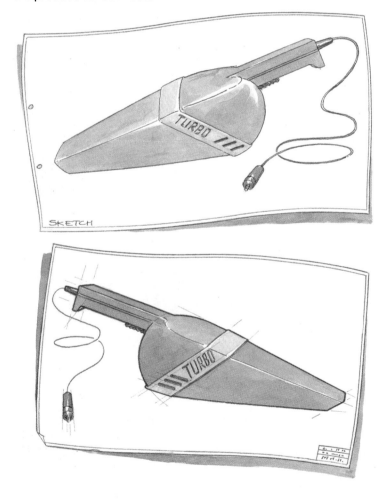

Pictorial views include **perspective** sketches. These are a very good means of communicating ideas in a general way. They let other people know what your designs might be like. Often sketches are used by designers to show several ways of solving a problem. The customer can then make a decision on the best idea at an early stage in the design process.

Perspective sketches may be drawn free-hand. The perspective can be judged by eye and the shapes adjusted until they look right.

A good measured perspective drawing takes more time to do than a sketch, but shows the appearance of the product more accurately and in greater detail. This is usually the next stage in drawing a pictorial view when one idea has been chosen.

Layouts

Design layouts are simple plans and elevations. They usually show the overall dimensions and can be coloured to show important features. They help to communicate general information at an early stage in the design. Designers often use design layouts with perspective sketches as the first stage of presenting a design.

General arrangements

General arrangement drawings are orthographic projections which give much more detail than design layouts. They show all the component parts of the article assembled and should have the hidden detail and sectional views necessary to explain the design.

Parts drawings

Before your design can be made, drawings are needed for all the separate parts. These are called parts drawings. Every detail needed to make each part must be included in these – for example, the exact dimensions of each part must be shown.

Parts drawings must be clear. The engineer or toolmaker who makes the component parts should be able to understand them easily. If you present your information poorly, or the details are unclear, then the end product is likely to be wrong. This can be a very expensive mistake.

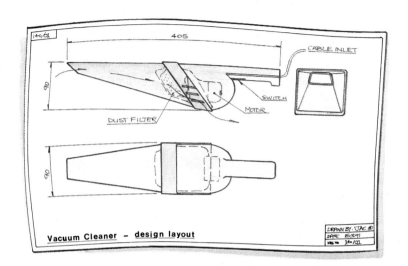

Vacuum Cleaner – design layout

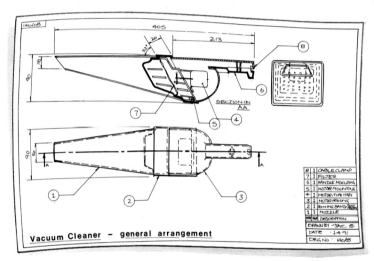

Vacuum Cleaner – general arrangement

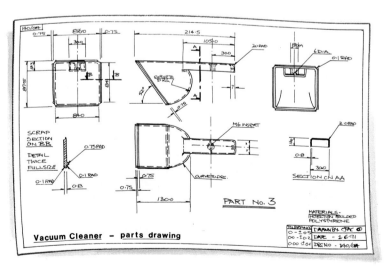

Vacuum Cleaner – parts drawing

Communicating with models 1

Models will communicate ideas more accurately than even the best drawings. A well-made model will tell people the size and form of the object and show the surface finish, texture, and colour. Some models are made to be so accurate that even the weight and balance are right, and the model feels exactly as if it is the finished product.

Just as there are different drawings appropriate to each stage in the design, there are also different types of model.

Sketch models

At an early stage in the design, modelling is a good way of trying out ideas. Sketch models can be used in the same way as sketch sheets to explore many possibilities. These models are sometimes referred to as concept models. They are usually made very quickly out of a material that can be worked easily, such as card, foamed polystyrene, or clay.

By making even a very simple model you can quickly see whether your design looks right. Is it the right size and proportions? What colours look good? These can easily be tried, and changed if necessary, using sketch models.

Sketch models also allow you to be sure that you are not being fooled by your own perspective sketches. Sometimes they can even replace perspective sketches. Designers often use sketch models at the initial design presentation, together with the design layout. They help the customer to understand the ideas being proposed.

Block models

A block model is usually the next stage in modelling. A block is more accurate than a sketch model. It must be exactly the same in outward appearance as the finished product will be. But, as the name suggests, it can be made from a solid block of material with all the internal details missing and with no moving or working parts.

The block model allows people to see all the external details of the design. It should show all the surface details, including any screws and joints, and have the correct texture and colour. It should be as faithful a representation of your design as you can make.

It is not difficult to build an accurate block model – it just takes time and patience. Because so much time has to be spent in building an accurate block model, it is important to decide on the final design, using drawings and sketch models, before you start.

Making changes to block models is not easy. Extra time spent at the sketch stage making final decisions may save you wasting time later on. In industry very accurate block models are used, not only to evaluate the design, but also for photographs for advertisements and brochures before the final product is ready.

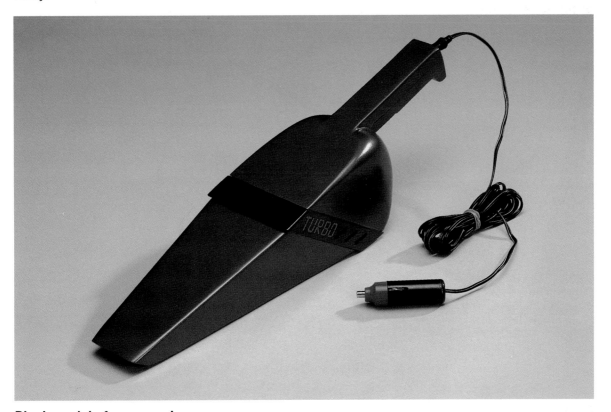

Block model of vacuum cleaner

Communicating with models 2

Working models

Working models need all the surface detail to be accurate in the same way as block models do. In addition, they will have moving or working parts. Depending upon the product to be modelled, a working model may need to be hollow, in order to contain batteries or a printed circuit board. It may need to unfold, have a hinged lid, or be taken apart.

These features will need to be made accurately, but many internal details can be ignored. For example, if you were building a working model of a battery-operated vacuum cleaner, your model would have to represent an injection moulding to house a motor and battery. So it would need enough space inside to hold these working parts. But unless the important features to show were the fixing details of the motor and battery, then your housing would not need all the moulding lugs and details that would be present on the inside of an injection moulded housing.

Working model

Inside of the working model

Prototypes

Prototypes are a much more complicated type of model. Unlike working models, they are made from the same material as that specified for the finished product. All external and internal detailing are included. They are identical in every way to the finished product except that they are **fabricated** by hand.

Prototypes are used a lot in industry to prove that the design of a product is right before expensive tools are made to mass produce it.

Inside of a prototype casing

A
S
S
I
G
N
M
E
N
T
S

● When might you use a sketch model of a design?

● What types of drawing will you need to produce to explain your ideas before you can begin building a block model?

● List five products for which it would be better to build a working model rather than just a block model. For each product, describe the possible advantages and disadvantages of a working model and a block model.

Right for the job

There is a wide variety of materials suitable for building a model. Which material you choose depends upon which type of model you are building and what shapes you need to make. In general terms, the softer the material and the easier it is to cut then the harder it is to maintain accurate lines.

Soft materials

Engineering materials

Materials such as foamed plastic or wood are easy to work but cannot be held to precise definition – they cannot be cut and shaped accurately and as planned. Engineering materials such as metal and rigid plastic are more difficult to cut and shape, but they are capable of fine definition, and do not damage easily. The surface on these engineering materials needs little finishing compared with foamed plastic and wood, and it is much easier to achieve a professional looking model with them.

Because of this, soft materials are useful for sketch models, which need to be built quickly and where surface finish is not important. But hard materials should be used whenever possible for precise block models.

The size and shapes you need to achieve are also an important factor when deciding which materials to use. There are some shapes that cannot be built in metal or plastic. It would be quite impractical to produce some large, very curved shapes in anything harder than wood, even for an accurate block model – see page 13. The chart on page 62 gives a summary of materials and their uses.

Cardboard

Cardboard is an excellent material for sketch models. It is easy to cut and bend, and can be glued together to make thick sections or joints – see pages 62–3. Cardboard can be painted or sprayed to colour it. You can draw on it with felt tip pens, markers, or coloured pencils to indicate joints and surface details such as ribs or switches. All these qualities make it ideal for simple models and flat shapes.

There are lots of different types of card available. They range in quality from strawboard, which is usually grey, to high quality art boards, with a good surface and choice of colour. Corrugated boards can be useful for their texture as well as strength.

Foamed plastics

Foamed plastics are very useful for building sketch models, especially those that have curved shapes. There are several different types and grades of foamed plastic.

Expanded polystyrene ...

Expanded polystyrene is a coarse-grained, white material available in block or sheet form. It is only suitable for sketch models because of its grain. This tends to crumble and makes it difficult to achieve a good surface finish.

... after it has been filled

This material can be cut quite successfully with a hot wire or knife, but a saw will give a very crumbly finish. The surface can be filled with a water-based filler such as plaster of Paris, and sealed with a water-based paint. Many household paints are suitable for this, including emulsion paint.

Styrofoam

Styrofoam is a fine-cell expanded polystyrene foam, usually white but sometimes blue. It is available in a standard or high density grade. High density Styrofoam is more closely packed, but both have a very fine grain structure. This makes Styrofoam far less crumbly than polystyrene, so it is much better for making models. It can be painted with water-soluble paints and glued with PVA adhesive – see page 63.

Like polystyrene, Styrofoam is best cut with a hot wire cutter or knife. But unlike polystyrene it can also be cut quite well with a band saw or hacksaw to give an acceptable surface.

Warning   Cutting expanded polystyrene and Styrofoam with a hot wire generates toxic styrene fumes. It should only be carried out in a well-ventilated room, and the wire should be set to operate below red heat.

Wood and wood products

Wood is a strong and durable material useful for building sketch models, particularly those that are large or need to last a long while. It is also useful for building more precise block models that have large curved shapes, as it can be built up into thick sections and these curves shaped easily.

Wood can be bonded together with a variety of adhesives – see page 63. The type you choose depends on how permanent a joint you need. Wooden dowels can be inserted across the joint to strengthen it. This stops the pieces slipping when they are clamped together.

The most suitable types of wood for model-making purposes, and the easiest to cut and shape, are those that are soft and have a straight grain, such as Jelutong. Once shaped, the surface of the wood can be primed and filled and a very smooth surface finish can be achieved. It is possible to simulate even the high gloss of a plastic moulding. However, to produce such a finish is very time consuming, and wood should only be considered for this type of finished model if the shape is too difficult to produce in an engineering material.

Straight grained woods

MDF (medium density fibreboard) is a flat, compressed board available in several thicknesses. It does not warp and is easy to cut and shape. This makes it ideal as a material to use for quick models.

Being so soft and porous, however, means that it damages easily. As with wood, although it is possible to produce a good surface finish it will take a lot of patient work.

MDF has a very smooth surface

Rigid plastics

Acrylic is one of the most widely used materials for building block models, and highly professional results can be achieved using it. The basic structure can be formed by fabricating sheet acrylic to form a shell or by machining from solid section, or by a combination of the two.

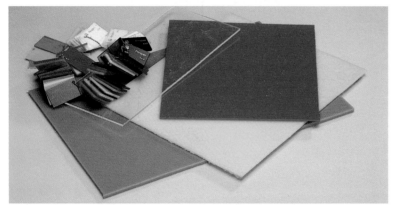

Many colours and textures are available in acrylic

Acrylic can be cemented easily

The distortion that occurs when acrylic is bent

There are few moulded parts that cannot be simulated with acrylic. Generally the only shapes unsuitable are large pieces with compound curves – see page 13.

Acrylic is flat and rigid, has a hard surface with a good finish, can be cut and stuck together, and machines well to form intricate shapes. It is a **thermoplastic**, and is available in a wide range of thicknesses in sheet form. If thick section acrylic is not available, sheet material can be laminated (bonded) together to build up any thick sections needed.

It is available in a wide range of colours both opaque and transparent, and with a gloss, matt, or textured surface.

Acrylic can be bonded very successfully using one of the tensol cements – see page 63. It can be tapped and screwed into to form mechanical fastenings. This can be useful when joining to a dissimilar material or when the model needs to be taken apart.

The surface of acrylic needs little preparation before painting, and it is easy to produce a very glossy finish.

Like other thermoplastics, acrylic can be heated and formed either on a line bender or in a simple press. But both these processes will cause distortion and are not generally suited to accurate model making.

Polystyrene is a thermoplastic with a hard, almost metallic surface. It is available in various thicknesses in standard sheet form, in gloss and matt finish, and in a wide range of colours.

Polystyrene, like acrylic, can be cut and fabricated to build models. It is the material most plastic model kits are made from and it can be bonded using the cements and solvents available for these toys – see page 63. The fumes from these cements and solvents can, however, soften the surface of the polystyrene and damage the surface finish.

Although polystyrene can be cut and fabricated quite easily it does not machine well. It has a low softening point and it is difficult to avoid local areas of melting by the tool and to achieve a good finish.

Polystyrene is most usually used in thin section for vacuum formed parts. However, **vacuum forming** as a process is generally only useful in

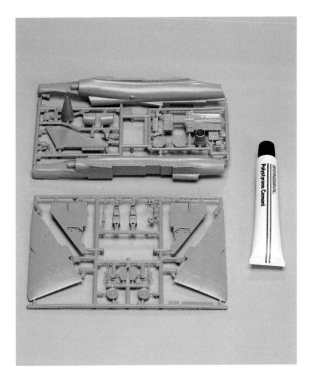

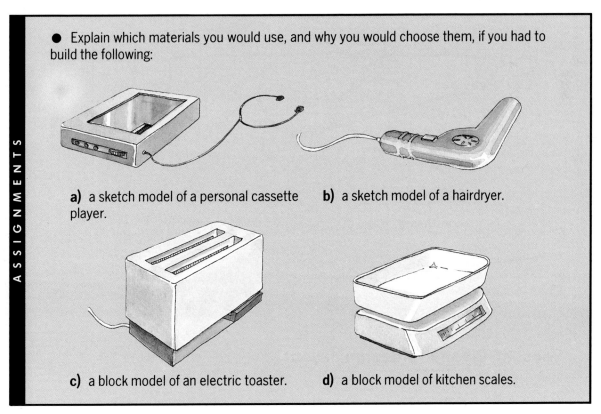

ASSIGNMENTS

● Explain which materials you would use, and why you would choose them, if you had to build the following:

a) a sketch model of a personal cassette player.

b) a sketch model of a hairdryer.

c) a block model of an electric toaster.

d) a block model of kitchen scales.

Starting off

The first stage in model making is usually a sketch model. Sketch models are useful for solving problems and trying ideas – a sort of three-dimensional sketch sheet. They should be able to be built quickly and used to develop ideas, so that if you change your design you can amend your model – or quickly build another.

The materials used for sketch models are those which can be easily worked. The final finish is not so important as the speed at which you can build and see your design in three dimensions (3D).

When you have lots of ideas for your design on your sketch sheets, draw a quick plan and elevation of the idea you think is best to make sure the design is feasible. Then, to make sure that the shapes look good in 3D, that the sizes and proportions are correct, and that you are not being fooled by your drawings, you will need to build a sketch model.

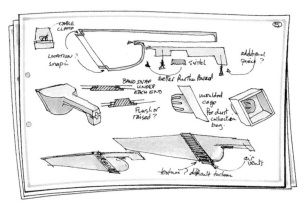

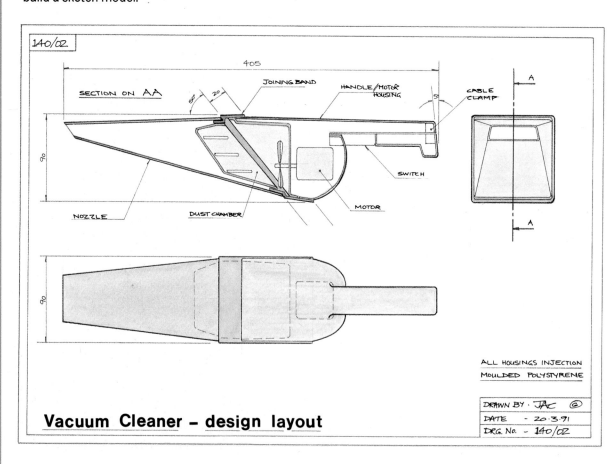

Vacuum Cleaner – design layout

Flat shapes

1 Draw the development of the part (part 2 – see page 22) on to the card.

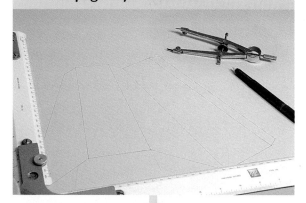

The flat, square shapes of your model are easiest to make from cardboard.

The **development** or unfolded shape can be constructed from the plan and elevation. It must be drawn accurately, otherwise it will not fold into the correct shape. Don't forget to leave some extra material for folds and flaps to glue the shape together.

Use a sharp craft knife for straight cuts in thick material and a scalpel for cutting thin board and curves. Scissors are not suitable for cutting card. They do not cut straight and they tend to buckle the card.

2 Cut around the drawn shape.

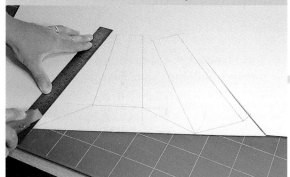

3 Crease the card where you want it to fold.

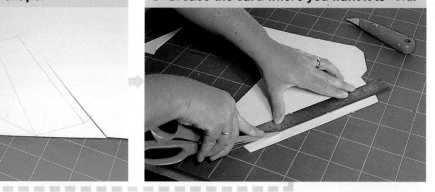

4 Make sure it folds into the correct shape.

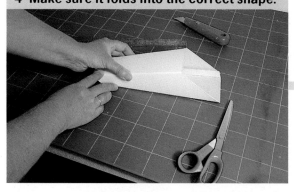

Double-sided sticking tape is suitable for a temporary joint. If your model has to last a long while, glue will give a more permanent joint – see page 63. Clothes pegs and paper clips are useful little clamps to hold the card together while the glue sets.

5 Glue it together using the flaps that you left for this purpose.

Curved shapes

The curved shapes on your model, which in production might be injection moulded in a rigid plastic, can be built quickly from a foamed plastic block, such as expanded polystyrene or Styrofoam. These materials can be cut easily and changed if necessary until you like the shape.

1 Draw the outline plan on to the top of the block of polystyrene (part 1 – see page 22).

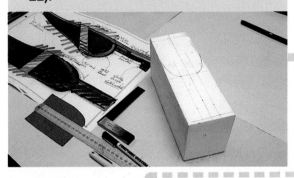

2 Cut around the shape with a band saw or hot wire cutter.

3 Draw the elevation on to the side, then cut around this.

4 Sand (see page 44) to round off the corners, judging the curves by eye.

Checklist for a part you have made

■ is it comfortable to hold?

■ are you able to reach any switches, levers etc.?

■ do you like the shape?
When you can see the three-dimensional form, assess the shape and change it if necessary.

5 Drill any holes needed – for example, for an electric cable.

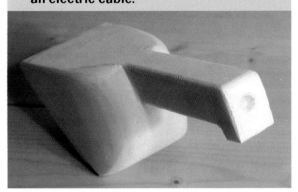

Preliminary assembly

Hold the parts of your model together with masking tape and look at the product you have designed and built.

Although very rough at this stage, the model should let you see whether the design looks right. Ignore the rough finish, and look critically at the proportions. Do the shapes look good now they are together? Does the model feel right?

Amend your design if necessary. Although you have spent some time building this sketch model, it is better to change the design now and build another model rather than carry any faults on through to further stages.

● From card draw out, cut, and fold the shape for a personal cassette player. Assess the result. Does it fit together and feel right? What improvements could you make?

● Use a block of expanded polystyrene to help you design and make the most comfortable shape you can for a hand-held object such as a hairdryer.

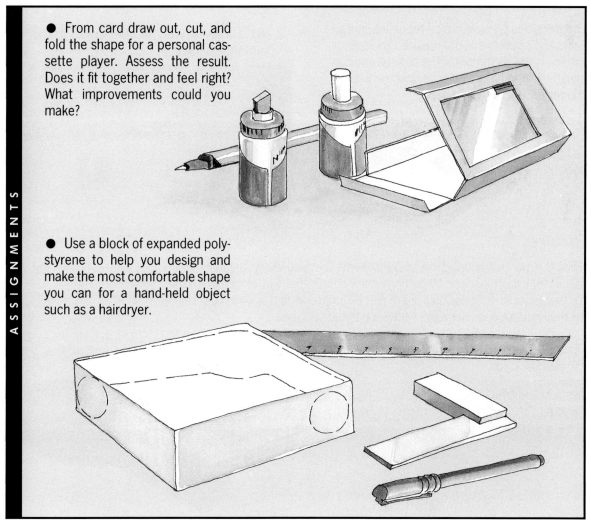

Painting/features

Painting

When you have produced a model you are happy with, carefully peel the masking tape off and prepare the parts for painting.

1 Fill any holes in the polystyrene with a water-based filler – see page 46.

This filling and priming can be repeated until all dents and cracks have disappeared and the surface is flat and smooth. The polystyrene can then be finished by painting or spraying with an enamel or a water-based paint.

The cardboard part will need no preparation and can be painted with a brush or roller, or sprayed. See pages 36–43 for more details on paints and painting.

2 When dry, rub it down with medium glass paper, then with fine.

3 Use a water-based paint to prime it – to seal the surface.

Features

When the model is painted in a colour scheme that you like, you can make the shapes look more realistic by putting on the details that would appear on the finished product. Practise on a spare piece of material first and make sure that the pen you use does not react with the painted surface.

1 Draw the joint lines with a pencil or marker pen.

2 Draw any switch/lever etc. and any screws that would show.

Assembly

Then you need to assemble the model in finished form.

1 Glue the separate parts of the model together – see page 63.

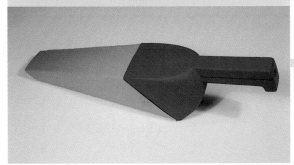

2 Cut any trim (part 3 – see page 22) from paper or foil and draw on the features.

3 When the glue is dry, stick trim around joints with double-sided sticking tape.

4 Glue any cable into the drilled hole with some PVA adhesive.

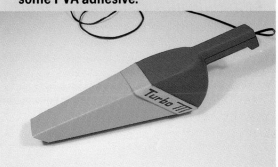

Your model should enable you to assess the size and proportions, the colours and general appearance of your design. Together with the design layout it can form part of the initial design presentation.

ASSIGNMENTS

● Use filler and paint to finish off the expanded polystyrene sketch model you made in the last assignment. Try to create the illusion of a plastic moulding.

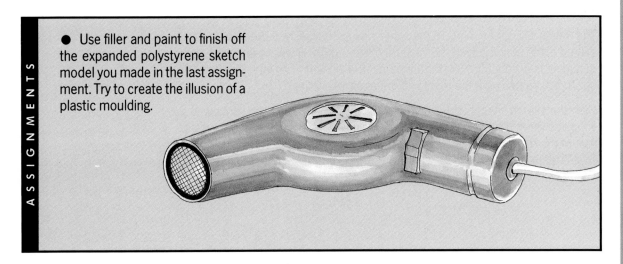

Designing the model

When your design layout, or general arrangement drawing, is finished, you will have all the details sorted out and the dimensions finalized. If you are pleased with your design, you may need to make a block model to present your ideas fully.

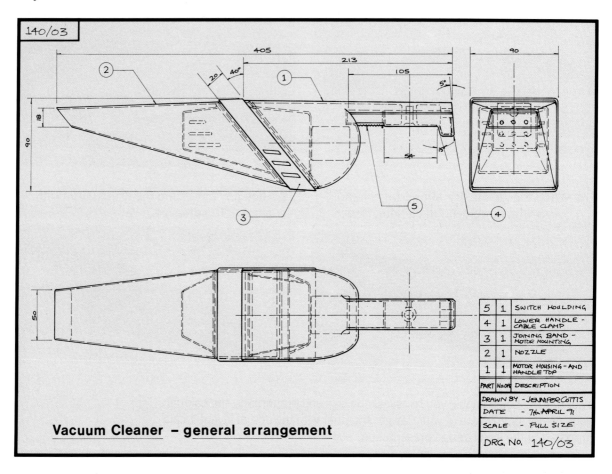

Vacuum Cleaner – general arrangement

The model will not be made in the same way as the finished product. In this example, the main body of the vacuum cleaner (part 1) will be an injection moulding in production. But for the model the illusion of an injection moulding has to be created with the tools and materials available.

Use your sketch sheets to design the block model in exactly the same way as you used them to design your product. Designing the model is an important part of the design process. Spending time at this stage in sketching can save time later in building.

When designing a model there are a number of questions you need to think about.

1 How strong must the model be?
If your model has to last, it is worth spending the extra time in building to make it strong. If it is for a photograph it may only be needed for a short time, and you may even be able to leave one side unfinished.

2 Which materials would be most suitable?
Some materials are difficult to finish, so although they may appear to be the easiest to work they can turn out to be the most time consuming – see page 62.

3 How will the model be constructed?
The materials you have chosen need to be cut and the pieces joined together to make each part. These parts or sub-assemblies will then have to be joined together to make the finished model.

4 Which processes will produce the most accurate model in the least time?
It is best to use machines wherever possible to cut the pieces for your model. Not only is it quicker but it will give the most accurate results. For example, a machine can be set to cut the correct angle, and that will then be consistent for every cut. Work out which machines you will use to produce the pieces.

5 How will you produce curved shapes?
Wood or MDF are the most suitable materials to build curved parts of a block model from.

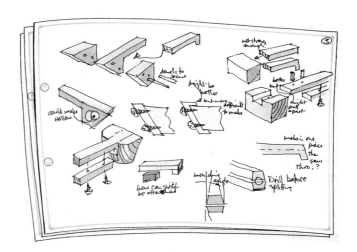

A solid block of wood could be used. But this may result in a heavy model. If the parts are large a better solution is to construct a box section of wood which could then be shaped. Decide on the easiest way to construct this section and the joints to use. Think ahead to the later stages of shaping the part. It is not a good idea to put the box together with screws as these may get in the way when you start to cut the curved profile.

A glued joint alone may not be strong enough. A better joint is one that is dowelled as well as glued. The dowels make the joint much stronger. They also make it easier to clamp the pieces of wood together when the glue is wet and slippery. The dowels help the pieces to stay where you want them and they will not be a problem later when you come to shape the curves.

(continued on page 24)

Questions to ask yourself 1

(continued from page 23)

6 How will you produce flat shapes?
Acrylic sheet is the easiest material to build flat or box shapes of a block model from.

This will also need to be cut and the pieces joined together. Decide which pieces to overlap and how to make the tidiest joints. To make the joints strong enough you may need to reinforce them with other small pieces of acrylic on the inside. This will give the acrylic cement more surface area to stick. It will also allow any small internal radii to be shaped.

Having made a decision about the materials and joints, draw a cutting plan of the pieces you will need to build each part. A cutting plan is like a dressmaking pattern. It gives you the sizes and shapes and shows the allowance for joining pieces together, ready to transfer to the material.

Put the dimensions on your cutting plan and make notes to remind you which pieces overlap and how they fit together.

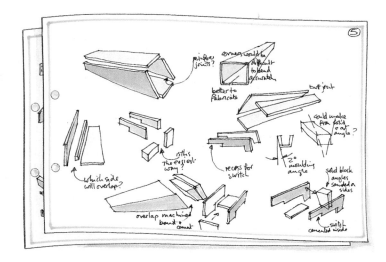

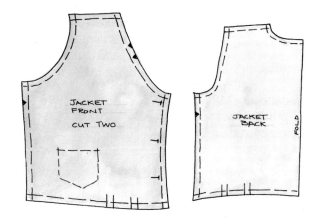

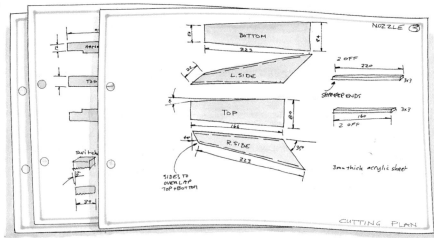

Planning the work

When working out a plan of action first check that any materials you need are available and decide what processes you will use (see pages 23–4).

The work generally falls into groups. In this example, these are: assemblies made from wood (part 1), assemblies made from acrylic sheet (parts 2 and 4), and parts that are machined from solid (parts 3 and 5).

Because of the long setting time for acrylic cement it is best to build the acrylic assemblies first, together with any parts which have to be laminated to get the necessary thickness. The glue and cement will then have plenty of time to set completely before you start any machining or finishing operations.

Work out which parts you should start first and decide on the best order for the cutting and shaping operations involved for each assembly. It is a good idea to draw a chart of the operations involved so that you can see at a glance how your model is progressing:

1 Start by listing the parts or sub-assemblies that you will have to make.

2 Find out how many weeks or lessons you have and mark these as columns on a bar chart.

3 List all the operations involved in building and machining and draw these operations as bars on the chart.

4 Estimate how long each operation will take and work out the order that all the operations should be done in.

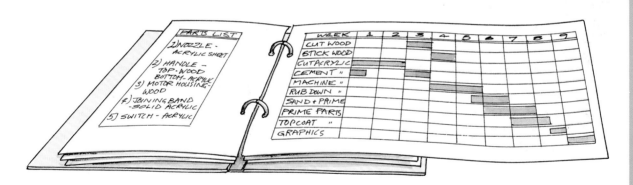

Careful planning will save you wasting a lot of time later in the workshop.

● Look again at this page and pages 23–4. Then, on a task you are starting, think carefully about all the factors that are important when choosing materials and designing a model. Design a model and draw up a cutting plan for each of the parts. Work out the best order of work and draw up a plan of action for the model you are going to make.

Marking out

Transfer the diagrams from your cutting plans to the materials that you are going to use for the model. Marking out must be done accurately if all the pieces are to fit together.

Marking-out tools

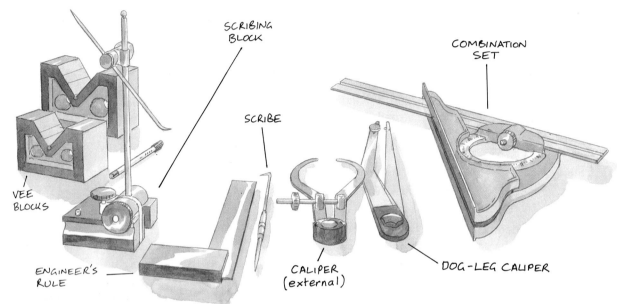

SCRIBING BLOCK

COMBINATION SET

SCRIBE

VEE BLOCKS

ENGINEER'S RULE

CALIPER (external)

DOG-LEG CALIPER

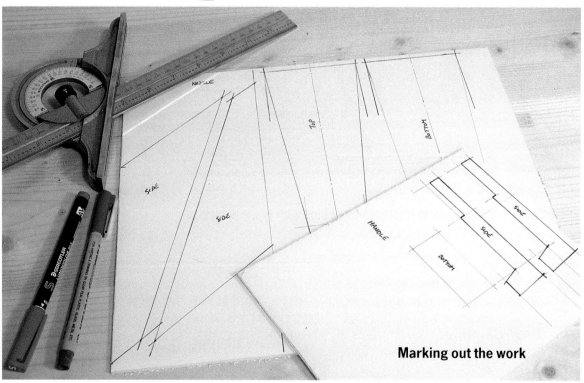

NOZZLE

TOP

BOTTOM

SIDE

SIDE

TOP

SIDE

SIDE

HANDLE

BOTTOM

Marking out the work

Laminating thick sections

It is best to laminate any thick sections that are needed for the model first, so that the cement has plenty of time to set before you start machining or finishing operations.

1 Cut the pieces quite a lot bigger than you need.

2 Remove the protective covering and apply the cement.

3 Using protective wooden blocks ...

Do not put G cramps directly onto the acrylic, as this will cause stress marks. Always put a piece of thick wood or metal between the G cramp and the acrylic to spread the load.

4 ... clamp the pieces together.

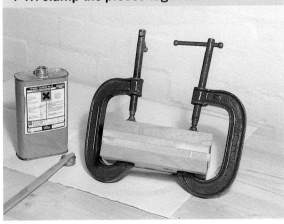

5 Another clamp across the ends will stop them sliding around. Leave to set completely – about seven days.

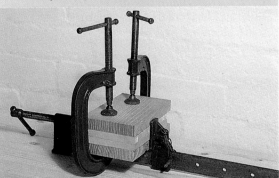

Assemblies from acrylic

1 Cut out the shapes for your model.

Cutting shapes from acrylic is easiest on a band saw. This puts less strain on the material than holding the piece and cutting it by hand with a hacksaw, so it will be less likely to crack the acrylic. A band-saw blade with ten **TPI** is best for acrylic. One that is much coarser will tend to chip the material, and a very fine blade will sometimes clog and weld itself in the cut.

2 Sand the pieces to the line on the disc sander.

3 Drill any holes you need for cable and switches/levers etc.

4 Cut recesses for switches/levers etc.

5 Clamp the acrylic between two pieces of strip steel.

6 Using the steel as a guide, smooth off the sawn edges.

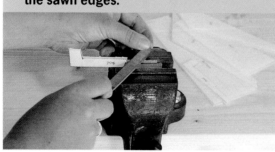

7 Check the sizes.

8 Cut reinforcing strips from scrap acrylic.

9 Cement the pieces together.

10 Hold them in place for a few minutes until the cement starts to set.

11 Cement a reinforcing strip along each joint.

12 Cement the other pieces together.

13 Put elastic bands around the assembly to apply gentle pressure while the cement sets.

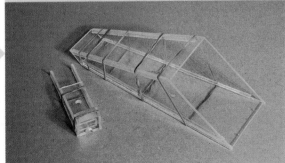

Before you put the assemblies in a safe place for the cement to harden, check that the pieces still line up and the angles on the sides are correct.

Assemblies from wood and wood products

1 Cut the shapes slightly oversize.

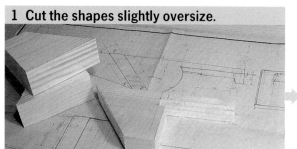

2 Clamp the pieces together.

3 Check what size wooden dowel is available and drill suitably sized holes through the clamped pieces.

4 Cut the dowels and glue the assembly together.

5 Clamp with some packing and leave to dry.

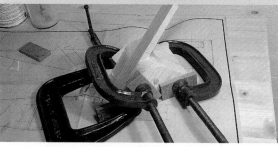

6 Sand or plane the top face flat.

7 Mark out the plan shape on the opposite side.

8 Cut around this shape.

9 Mark out the elevation shape onto the side.

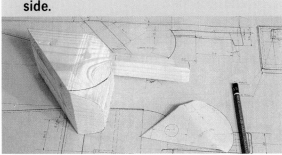

10 Cut around the elevation.

11 Check the dimensions and angles.

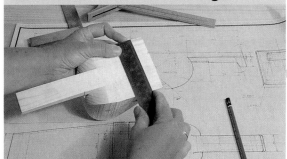

12 Drill any holes you may need.

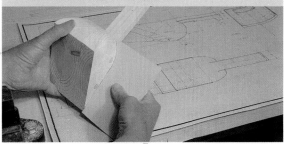

13 Blend in the curves with a coarse file.

14 Use a cardboard template to check that both sides are the same.

15 Sand until the file marks have gone.

16 Sand the small radii on the corners.

Machining parts from solid

Intricate parts can be machined from solid pieces of acrylic or aluminium (see page 62). The machine you use and the type of cutter will depend upon the shape you are trying to build.

In the example of the vacuum cleaner, part 5 (the switch button) is a simple piece to make. It can be cut very quickly on the vertical milling machine.

1 Cut the ends and sand them parallel and to length.

2 Hold these ends in the machine vice with the piece horizontal.

3 Put an end mill in the machine and set it to the correct speed.

4 Set the head of the machine to 45° and machine grooves across the top.

5 Then with the head at 2° – the moulding angle – machine one side.

6 Turn the piece around, hold horizontally, and machine the other side to the correct width.

Some of the parts you will need to make will of course be more complex than this. The shape needed for the vacuum cleaner trim (part 3) appears to be more difficult to make. In fact, it is fairly easy – it will just take a little more time.

Like the switch button, this joining band will be made on a vertical milling machine. But the machine that is used for this piece has no angular adjustment for the head.

1 Drill two fixing holes through the acrylic and a packing piece.

2 Bolt the angle plate to the bed of the machine.

3 Set the angle plate horizontally and bolt the acrylic to it.

4 Put an end mill in the machine and set to the height of the trim.

5 Machine the first side of the recess and check the depth.

6 Machine other sides without altering the height setting.

These first cuts have only machined the face and will have to be repeated later with the correct side angle of the nozzle set.

7 Raise the bed and machine the sides.

8 Tip the angle plate to the side angle of the nozzle.

9 Reset the height and machine the angle on the flange.

10 Repeat this for the other side.

11 Move the work away from the cutter, unbolt and turn through 90°.

12 Bolt it down loosely and adjust to be at exactly 90° to the previous setting.

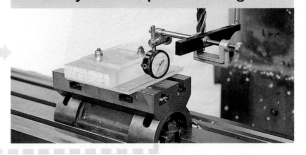

13 Set the angle plate for the remaining angle.

14 Machine the other sides in the same way as the first two.

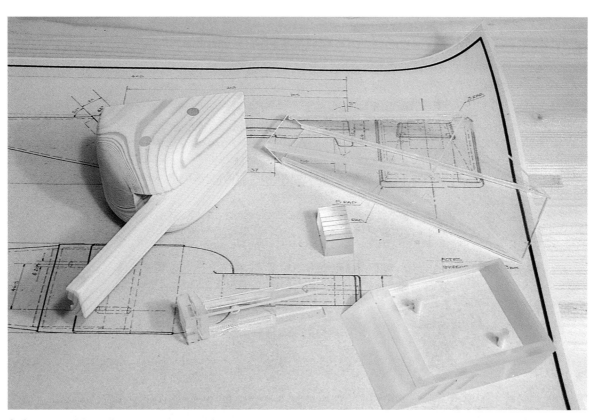

Sub-assemblies for the vacuum cleaner

● Imagine you are going to make a torch model from acrylic.

a) Which tools will you need to mark out the necessary pieces?

b) List the operations needed to build the torch casing.

c) What are the stages necessary to machine the handle from solid acrylic?

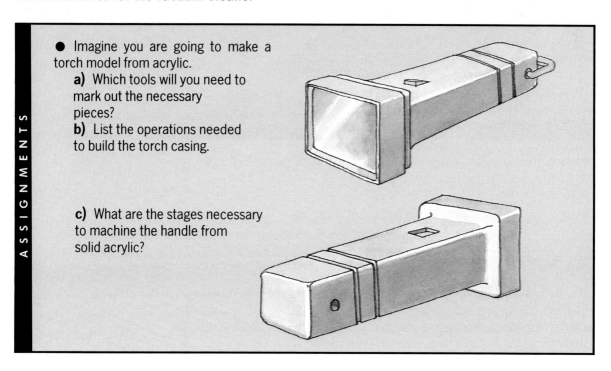

Choosing the paint: cellulose

Most of the parts that you make for a model will need to be painted. There are several types of paint available. Some are easier to use and more versatile than others – see page 39 for a summary.

Cellulose

Cellulose paint is used in the car industry, both for mass-produced and hand-crafted vehicles, to produce a high gloss finish. Because it is used so widely for painting car bodies, it is available in a large range of colours and shades. Cellulose paint and primer are available in tins for brushing or spraying and in aerosol cans from most DIY car repair shops.

Cellulose dries extremely quickly. It is touch dry in a few minutes and can safely be rubbed down after ten or fifteen minutes. This makes it very convenient to use.

Cellulose paint, like most paints, is best used on top of the same material primer – it reacts with some other primers. It bonds to cellulose primer and will give a hard durable finish, provided it is applied in thin coats which are allowed to dry.

Cellulose paint and primer can be put on most materials, but they dissolve expanded polystyrene and some grades of polystyrene sheet. They should not be put on expanded polystyrene unless you are sure that a suitable water-based primer has completely covered the surface.

Enamels, such as those sold by Humbrol for model-makers, are available in very small tins and miniature spray cans. The range of colours available in these small tins of enamel is fairly limited when compared with cellulose. However, many household paints are also enamel (their labels will tell you which ones), and this widens the range.

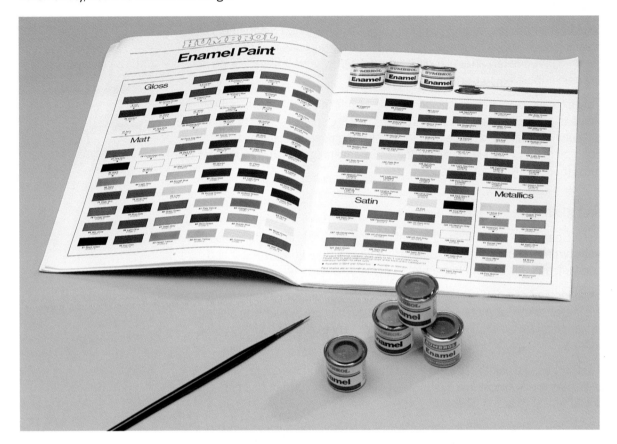

Enamel paints can be used over conventional household primers – see page 39. They can also be used on cellulose primer if it is left to dry completely first. (Enamel can be used over cellulose but cellulose cannot be used over enamel.)

Enamels can be thinned with white spirit or turpentine and sprayed quite successfully.

The main disadvantage of using enamel paints is that they are slow to dry. They often need between twelve and twenty-four hours to harden. Not only will a model painted with enamels take longer to finish, but there is a greater risk of dust ruining the surface before the paint is hard.

One advantage of using enamels is the very small quantities they are available in. This is useful if your model is small, or if there are buttons or controls in contrasting colours. Also, enamels do not react with expanded polystyrene and Styrofoam and can be used successfully on these materials.

Choosing the paint: enamel

Polyurethane

Polyurethane paints are widely used in industry because of their extremely tough finish. Most are of the twin-pack variety, with resin and hardener in separate tins. When these are mixed, a chemical reaction takes place that makes the paint harden.

Special thinners are required, and once the paint has dried the thinners and cleaning fluids will no longer work. Brushes and spray guns that are not cleaned immediately after use will be ruined. Spray guns left uncleaned may even be impossible to dismantle.

Polyurethane paint can usually be obtained from ships' chandlers, but the range of colours available is very limited. They are specialist paints and the difficulty in obtaining a range of colours, plus the need to clean all the equipment immediately, outweigh the small advantage of extra toughness for most model-making purposes.

Acrylic

Acrylic paint can be used on all model-making materials including expanded polystyrene. It covers well with a brush or can be thinned with water and sprayed, and takes about two hours to dry.

Small pots of one-part acrylic paint, such as those sold for painting model cars, are water soluble and completely safe to use. They are available in a good range of colours, including metallics, and are very useful for painting small models.

Two-part acrylic paints are used in the car industry and therefore, like cellulose, are available in a multitude of colours. They harden to a high gloss finish, similar to acrylic sheet.

Warning These two-part acrylic lacquers contain chemicals from the isocyanide family, which can attack the lungs and be extremely dangerous. If you are spraying these paints make sure you use a suitable breathing mask.

Paints, primers, and cleaners

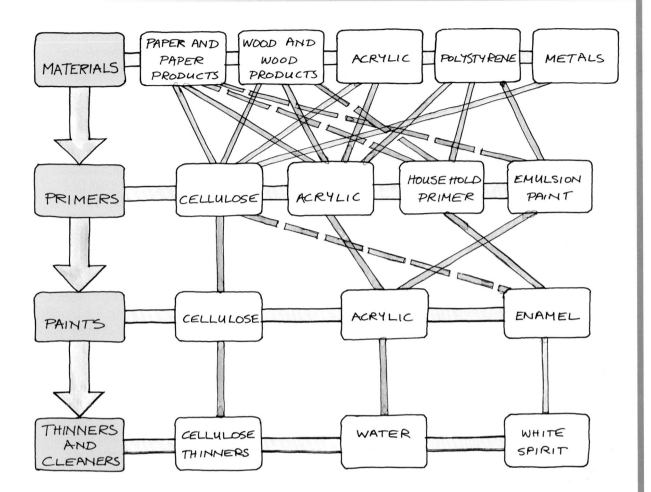

Whichever paint you use, it is always advisable before painting your model to test some on a piece of similar scrap material.

ASSIGNMENTS

● Which primers and paints could you use on a model made from expanded polystyrene? What are their advantages and disadvantages?

● Which paints would be most suitable for painting contrasting control knobs and buttons?

● From a model you are building, list the materials you have used and decide which paints, primers, and cleaners would be most suitable for it.

● Set up a simple test to show the effect different primers, paints, and cleaners have on different materials.

Applying the paint: handpainting

Whichever paint you are using, it will have to be applied to the model in a way that achieves the type of surface finish you want. You can put on the paint in several ways.

Handpainting

Paint can be applied to the model by hand with a soft paint brush or small paint roller. It is possible to achieve a good finish by hand, but it will take some time. The surface has to be rubbed down to remove brush marks, and to a lesser extent the marks of the roller, after each coat. (See chapters 8 and 9 for more information about sanding and finishing.)

The model has to be held fairly securely to keep it still while it is being painted and drying. It is usually necessary to put in additional screws or make a jig to hold each piece so that the paint surface is not damaged.

Several thin layers of paint are better than one thick one. It is very tempting to put on very thick coats of paint in an attempt to save time. But thick coats of paint will take longer to dry, and will almost always run and go into blobs, which will need sanding down.

It is far easier to achieve a professional finish by spraying the paint. There are several ways of doing this.

Aerosol cans

Aerosol cans of paint are suitable for spraying models, but the aerosol can is not an instant recipe for success. The model still has to be held. However, it does not need to be held still in the same way as when hand painting. The easiest way to hold the work, for any spraying operation, is to hang the parts on pieces of wire.

To avoid spatters and drips landing on the work, the can should be held horizontally. The spray should be started away from the model, moved across in an even movement, and stopped when it is pointing away from the model.

Several light coats are better than one thick one. Build up the paint in very thin layers, allowing each coat to dry before applying the next. This will avoid paint runs.

The distance the spray can is held away from the work will also affect the finish. Hold it too close, and you will get an 'orange peel' effect where too much paint floods on in one go. Hold it too far away and you will get a fine, dusty appearance where the paint is starting to dry in the air before it lands on the model.

The optimum distance for an aerosol can of cellulose paint is about 20 cm. The type of paint you are using, however, may be different, so experiment on some scrap material before you start spraying your model.

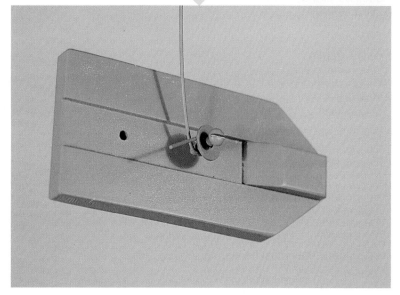

Applying the paint: spraying 1

Applying the paint: spraying 2

Most paints can be thinned to a suitable consistency and sprayed using an airbrush or spray gun.

Airbrushes

Graphics airbrushes are expensive. The airbrush needles, which control the flow of air and paint, are very fragile, and like the rest of the instrument they must be kept absolutely clean. They hold a small amount of paint, which makes them only suitable for small pieces of model. The degree of fineness which this type of airbrush can produce is rarely needed in model making.

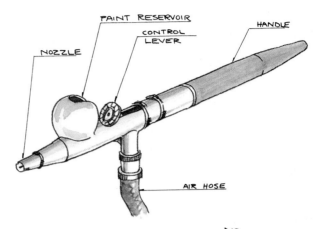

Needleless airbrushes are much cheaper and less prone to damage than graphics airbrushes. They usually have a greater capacity and are more suitable for model making. They are not capable of a very fine spray, but they can produce a reasonable finish on small models. An example is the Humbrol modellers' airbrush, which is really a mini spray gun.

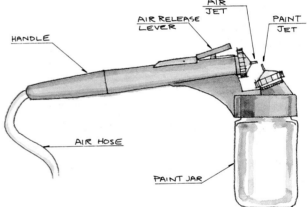

Spray guns

For large models you will probably need a spray gun, which is very similar to an airbrush. Most are operated with a single trigger. The initial trigger movement opens the air valve, and continuing movement back to an adjustable stop regulates the paint. Spray guns range in size from small lightweight guns, little larger than an airbrush, to large production models.

Once you have got used to using a spray gun it will give by far the best results. But like airbrushes, to work properly they must be kept absolutely clean.

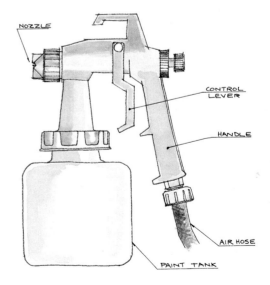

Applying the paint: spraying 3

To spray your model with a spray gun or airbrush you will need a supply of air as a propellant. Because of their small size, airbrushes and mini air guns need little air and can be used with canned propellant. Larger spray guns will need much more air and greater pressure, and an air compressor will be needed.

Avoid splatters and splashes when using an airbrush or spray gun in the same way as when you spray with an aerosol can: always spray horizontally, not down onto your work; start spraying away from the work; apply a thin coat, ending with the spray gun or airbrush pointing away from the model.

A small compressor is capable of running a spray-gun

Safety

Spraying paint gives the best result and is not dangerous if you always take basic safety precautions:

■ always wear a respirator/mask even if you are spraying non-hazardous paints – inhaling paint fumes and dust is harmful;

■ only spray in a well ventilated room or extraction cupboard;

■ do not spray near a naked flame – many paints are inflammable and many paint vapours are explosive.

● What is the easiest way to hold the parts of a model for spraying?

● A good spray finish is even and free of blemishes. Draw-up a 'code of good practice' that, if followed carefully, will provide you with a good spray finish. Do the same for handpainting.

Sanding

The various parts of the model will have to be finished off before they are ready for painting.

Sub-assemblies from acrylic

Acrylic parts need excess material removed from the joints.

1 A lot of the excess can be removed, with care, on a disc sander.

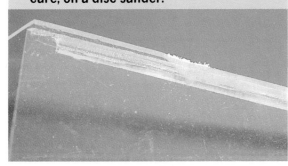

2 Remove small amounts with a fine file ...

3 ... followed by wet-and-dry paper — first coarse, then fine.

4 File external radii, then remove file marks with wet-and-dry paper.

5 Use fillers to make fillet radii.

6 Then file to shape, finishing with wet-and-dry paper.

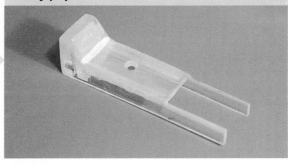

See pages 46–8 for more information on fillers and how to apply them.

1 Rub down with glass paper – first medium, then fine.

Sub-assemblies from wood

Wooden parts should be sanded as smooth as you can make them. As you work, check that the surfaces are flat and that the dimensions are correct. Enthusiastic sanding can remove quite a lot of material in a short time.

2 Seal the surface with a suitable sealer.

3 Sand again with fine glass paper. Repeat sealing and sanding until smooth.

Parts machined from solid

Machined parts should need little preparation before priming, but check that there are no burrs or very sharp corners.

1 Remove burrs with a very fine file or wet-and-dry paper.

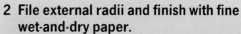

2 File external radii and finish with fine wet-and-dry paper.

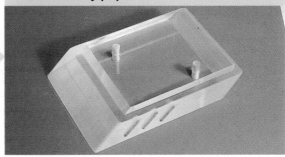

At this stage, check that the pieces of a model are smooth and fit together.
The next stage is painting.

Fillers

Fillers are very useful, but apply them sparingly. Avoid spreading them over a large area – it is hard work to remove them.

The main problem when using fillers is that they do not cure to the same hardness as the surrounding material. When you rub them down it is difficult not to get lumps and depressions, as the filler and surrounding model rub down at different rates.

There are different types of filler available. The best type to use for each part depends upon the size of the hole or area to be filled, the material the piece is made from, and the primer you have used.

Water-based fillers

These include plaster of paris and Polyfilla, and are very useful for filling holes, dents, and areas of coarse grain in expanded polystyrene. But these fillers are very soft and damage easily, which makes them less suitable for more permanent models.

Polyester-based fillers

Polyester fillers such as Isopon are used in repairing car bodies, and are available from DIY car suppliers. They come in two parts, filler and hardener. These have to be mixed until they are completely blended and no streaks remain.

These fillers remain usable for about ten minutes and can be rubbed down after about fifteen or twenty minutes, depending on how much hardener is used. Because they do not rely on evaporation to harden they can be used in very thick layers if necessary.

The surface of very smooth materials such as acrylic needs to be roughened for the filler to key, and for this reason polyester fillers are best used on bare material before the surface has been sealed, primed, or painted.

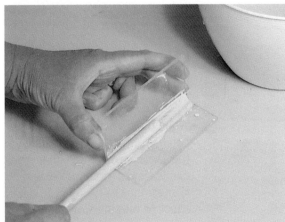

Smoothing epoxy filler

Epoxy fillers

Epoxy fillers are available as two-part resins. An example is Milliput, which is available from model-making shops and is supplied as two coloured putties. These have to be thoroughly blended until there are no streaks. When mixed they produce a fine filler, which bonds very well to most materials except expanded polystyrene.

Epoxy fillers take much longer to harden than polyester fillers, but this makes them more controllable. It is possible to achieve a very smooth finish by wetting the surface when smoothing off. This can be useful for fillet radii, which are always awkward to get into to rub down. The longer hardening time can be offset against the extra work that would be necessary to rub down polyester fillers, which are less controllable.

Like polyester, epoxy fillers do not rely on evaporation to harden and can therefore be used in thick layers. However, the difficulty in mixing large amounts makes them more suitable for small areas.

Cellulose fillers

These can be bought from DIY car suppliers, usually as a grey putty. They are very fine, often not much thicker than cellulose primer, and if used over cellulose primer they will bond to the primed surface.

Cellulose filler hardens through evaporation, so it is most suited to filling small blemishes after the surface has been primed (see page 49). Any deep cracks or holes should be built up in layers, allowing the cellulose filler to harden completely between layers – usually about fifteen minutes.

Warning   Keep the lid tightly on the tin when not in use – the putty will harden otherwise, and the fumes from it are harmful.

Applying the filler

The easiest way to apply the filler is with a small tool. Fingers are useful, but they soon get covered in putty, and then it is difficult not to spread it all over the model.

Use a piece of waste acrylic or mild steel strip or rod to make a tool. Shape one end to form a flat spatula and the other to a point. This will be useful for getting into gaps and cracks of most shapes. You can make tools of different shapes to suit particular models.

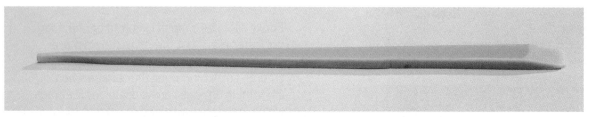

Be careful not to put on too much filler at a time. It is better to use it sparingly and add extra as necessary.

When the filler is dry and hard, it can be rubbed down in exactly the same way as the primer. You can then add more primer and filler as necessary, until you are satisfied with the surface.

ASSIGNMENTS

● Prepare a checklist to show which filler(s) is/are most suitable for using with commonly available materials before and after priming.

Priming

Whichever type of paint is going to be used for a final coat, the model must first be primed with a suitable primer (see page 39). Primer is a type of sticky, thick paint. Different types adhere well to the various materials, will seal the surface, and will allow you to see the small cracks, scratches, dips, and hollows that still remain.

Getting rid of dips and hollows

Make sure that the parts of the model are clean, dry, and free from dust and grease. Apply two or three coats of primer to each piece. Allow to dry and rub down with medium grade wet-and-dry paper, used wet.

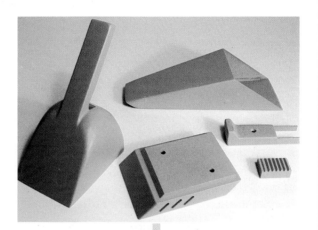

Use a sanding block on flat areas so as not to rub depressions into the work. If the piece is small or difficult to hold, put the wet-and-dry sheet onto a flat surface and rub the model onto this.

When the surface is flat and smooth, apply a coat or two of primer of a contrasting colour. When this is dry, rub down again. Any dips or hollows then show up clearly as a change in colour.

It is usually possible to eliminate hollows with a build-up of primer, rubbed down between every two or three coats. But any cracks between joints or small holes will have to be filled with a suitable filler. If there are any large holes or cracks in your sub-assemblies, they should be filled before you start painting, but small cracks and scratches will be best left until after a coat of primer.

Texture, paint, and polish

Not all products are designed to have a high gloss finish. You may need to simulate an area of moulded-in texture on your model.

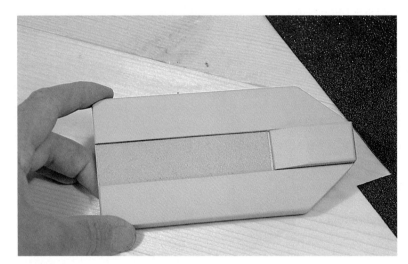

Small areas of texture

Flat, small, localized areas of texture are best achieved with add-ons.

Paper can be an excellent add-on material. Coarse or medium wet-and-dry paper can be used to create the type of surface texture often found on injection mouldings. The textured paper can be attached with adhesive or double-sided sticking tape to produce an area of relief or in an insert. A thin layer of primer then makes this appear to be an integral part of the model.

The type of die-cut sticky labels and letters found in stationers' can be used in the same way. Often the waste material from these types of sticker can produce useful effects.

Any of these paper areas can be rubbed down if necessary after they have been primed – but only use wet-and-dry paper dry, in case you rub through the primer.

Overall texture

Fine, overall areas of texture can be achieved with paint or primer.

In industry, some foamed mouldings often need painting. A fine 'crackle' finish is quite often applied to foamed polyurethane mouldings by spraying with a spatter nozzle on the spray gun. A similar effect can be achieved by reducing the air pressure and spraying with a normal nozzle.

Experiment with your spray gun and compressor to see what effects you can make.

It is also possible to get a spatter effect using an aerosol can of cellulose paint or primer. Try this, by only partially depressing the button on the aerosol can. With practice quite a consistent spatter can be obtained.

Spatter effect can be achieved with an aerosol can

Final coat

When you are satisfied with the primed finish on a model, then put on the coloured paint. Apply two or three layers of paint, allowing to dry between coats.

There should be no need to rub down the surface between coats. If the paint should run or blob, let it dry thoroughly before rubbing it down with wet-and-dry paper, first medium and then fine grade, both used wet. Make sure the water has dried, then apply another coat of paint.

High gloss finish

If you want a very shiny finish on your model this can be achieved by polishing the painted surface, after it has hardened, with rubbing compound or metal polish.

Rubbing compound is an abrasive wet paste, slightly coarser than metal polish, available from car DIY suppliers. Polish with a soft cloth until a high gloss is obtained.

Rubbing with metal polish or rubbing compound removes a very thin layer of paint. If you intend to polish your model, make sure it has several extra coats of paint.

Assembly

Areas of different colour

If your model is to be painted in two or more colours, the safest and most realistic method is to build it as separate pieces, spray them separately, and assemble them when dry.

Masking areas to achieve contrasting colours is generally unsuccessful.

1 The paint builds up against the masking edge and often bleeds under the edge.

2 When the tape is removed, it frequently pulls off a layer of paint.

Just when you think your model is nearly finished – disaster!

Final assembly

Assemble the finished parts without adhesive, and check that they fit together.

1 Remove any paint that has built up in the recesses with a sharp scalpel.

2 Assemble the parts with adhesive and leave until completely set.

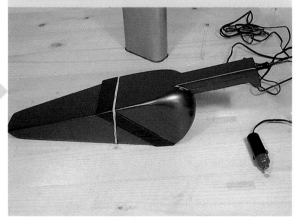

If your model has bolts or screws to fix it together, remember that they are part of the design, and choose those that look good and will not corrode.

If you look at products in the shops, you will see that they almost always have a brand name or logo in a prominent position. You can make your model look more realistic by adding product graphics.

A logo or brand name can be lettered directly onto the model, or applied as a label or a moulded-in feature. This brand image is part of the design, so its size, form, and position should be carefully thought out as part of the style and visual impact of the overall design.

Lettering

Applying a brand name directly onto the painted surface of the model is best done with rub-down lettering, such as Letraset. This is available in black, white, and primary colours in a wide range of type faces and sizes. There are also lines, borders, and hatching, which can be quite effective.

There is no risk of spoiling the paintwork, once it is hard, with this type of lettering. It can be easily removed if necessary with masking tape and the letters reapplied.

Rub-down lettering ...

... being applied ...

... and being removed with masking tape

Product graphics: labels and moulding

Labels

Labels can be made from many different materials. Paper, thin card, or a piece of thin plastic sheet are all suitable as backing material. This can be self-coloured, painted, or covered in foil to make a label.

The lettering can be applied to the label with rub-down lettering ...

... or with coloured pencils, markers, or paints.

Because the label is a separate part you can experiment with different colours and finishes, without any risk to the model, until you get one that you like. This can then be stuck on with double-sided sticking tape or a little impact adhesive.

Moulded-in lettering

Relief lettering can be achieved in the same way as small areas of texture, using die-cut stick-on letters with a layer of primer over the top.

Deeper relief can be achieved by using two or three layers of letters ...

... or logos can be cut from card and stuck on with adhesive.

ASSIGNMENTS

- On a model you are currently working on, how would you:
  a) create a small area of texture?
  b) produce a very shiny surface?
  c) add a brand name?

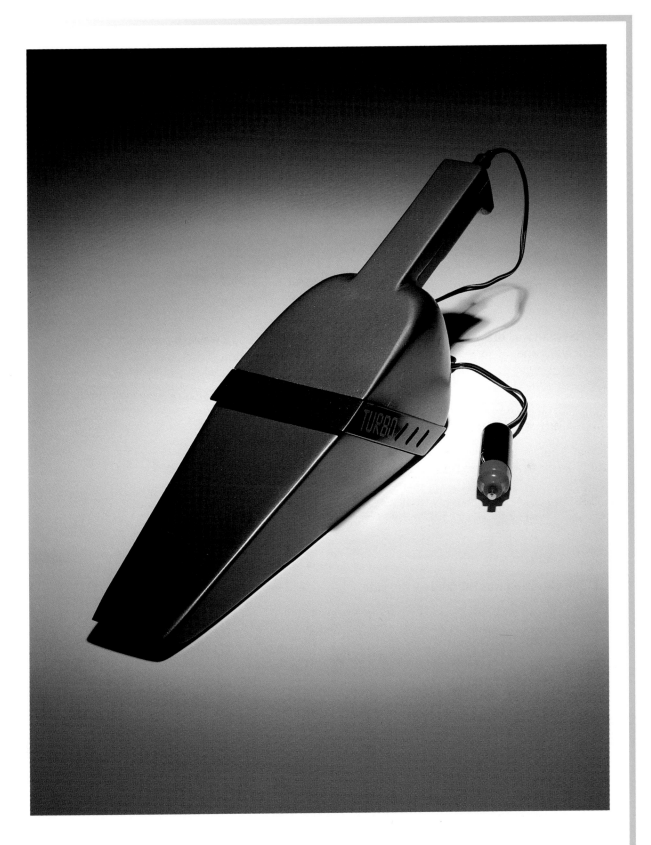

The finished model

Case study 1

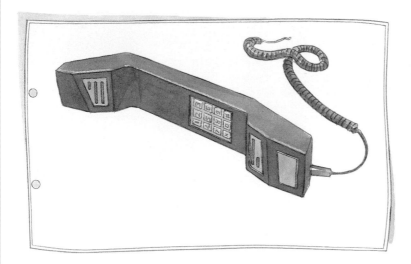

A design for a freestanding telephone needed to be modelled quickly to get the right shape and size for the handset, to check the proportions and appearance. A sketch model was made.

1 The plan was drawn on a block of polystyrene.

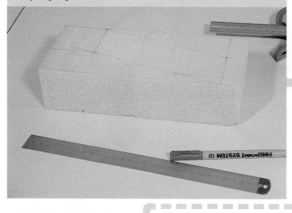

2 This shape was cut round with a hot wire cutter.

3 The elevation was marked on the side.

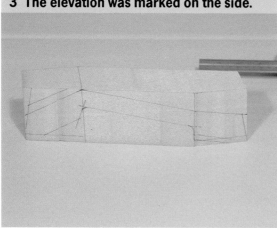

4 This shape was cut round.

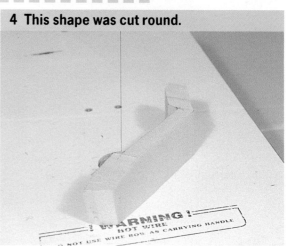

5 The curves were sanded with medium glasspaper.

6 The shape was assessed and amended.

7 Recesses for the grid and button were cut with a scalpel.

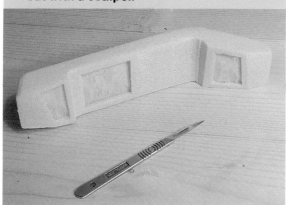

8 The hole for the cable was drilled.

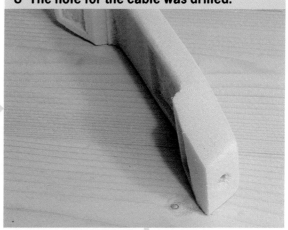

9 The shape was painted with emulsion paint.

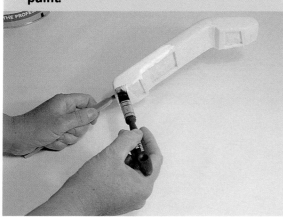

10 The grain was filled with plaster, sanded, and filled again until smooth.

11 The model was sprayed with enamel paint and left to dry.

12 Grids were made from thin card, with details drawn with fine-tipped pen and markers.

13 The finished model.

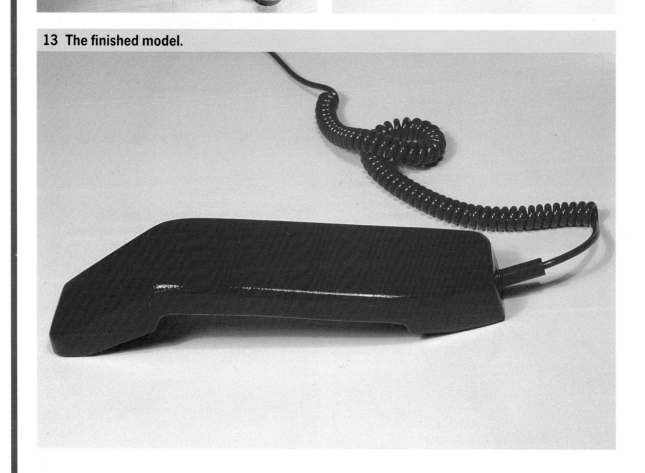

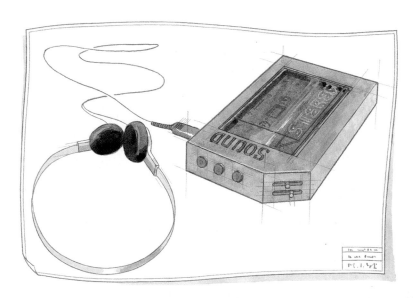

A design for a portable cassette player needed a realistic model to show fully the styling, size, and shape. A block model was made.

Case study 2

1 Acrylic was laminated to the right thickness and left to set thoroughly.

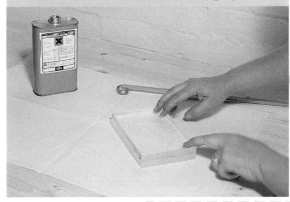

2 Fixing holes were drilled in the positions of the driving pins.

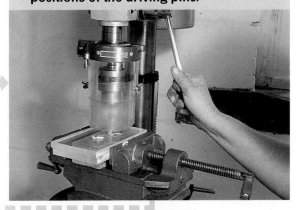

3 The block was bolted, with packing under it, to the bed of the milling machine.

4 With a suitable cutter, the four sides were machined.

5 One screw was removed, the work was turned, and the angled corner was machined.

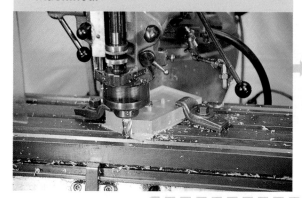

6 The work was transferred to a vice, and a recess for the cassette was machined.

7 The cutter was changed to machine the corners and face for the cover.

8 The work was turned over and a recess machined for the battery cover.

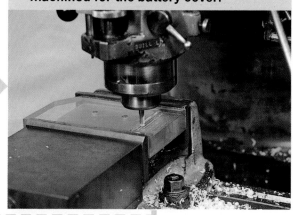

9 Holes were machined for push buttons and cables.

10 Acrylic rod was cut and glued in position for the driving pins.

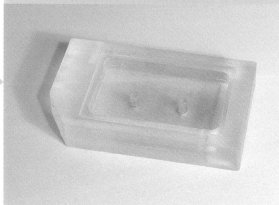

11 Pieces of acrylic were cut for covers and buttons.

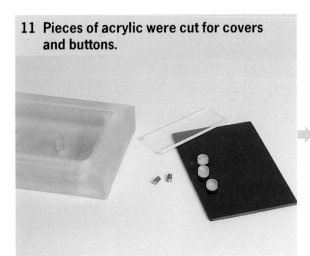

12 The battery cover was glued in position and the model primed.

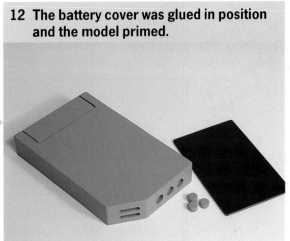

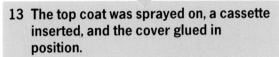
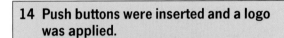

13 The top coat was sprayed on, a cassette inserted, and the cover glued in position.

14 Push buttons were inserted and a logo was applied.

Materials and uses

Key (USES):

✓✓✓	VERY USEFUL
✓✓	QUITE USEFUL
✓	SOMETIMES

MATERIALS	EASY TO WORK	EASY TO FINISH	SKETCH/DEVELOPMENT MODELS	BLOCK MODELS	WORKING MODELS	SURFACE TEXTURES	GRAPHICS TRIMS
PAPER PRODUCTS							
PAPER	✓✓✓	✓✓	✓✓			✓✓✓	✓✓
CARDBOARD	✓✓✓	✓✓	✓✓✓			✓✓✓	✓✓
CORRUGATED CARDBOARD	✓✓✓	✓	✓✓			✓✓	
PLASTICS							
EXPANDED POLYSTYRENE	✓✓		✓	✓✓	✓✓		
RIGID POLYSTYRENE	✓✓	✓✓✓		✓✓	✓✓		
ACRYLIC	✓✓	✓✓✓		✓	✓		
WOOD PRODUCTS							
WOOD	✓✓	✓		✓✓	✓✓		
PLYWOOD	✓✓	✓		✓	✓		
M.D.F.	✓✓	✓		✓✓	✓		
METALS							
ALUMINIUM	✓✓	✓✓✓			✓✓		✓✓✓
EXPANDED ALUMINIUM	✓					✓✓	✓✓
STEEL	✓✓	✓✓				✓	

Materials and adhesives

ADHESIVES

TYPE				BRAND NAME	FORM	CURE TIME	CLAMPING	GAP FILLING	PAPER PRODUCTS	EXPANDED POLYSTYRENE	RIGID POLYSTYRENE	ACRYLIC	WOOD PRODUCTS	ALUMINIUM
IMPACT				BOSTIC 3 / EVO STIK CONTACT	LIQUID	IMMEDIATE	LIGHT PRESSURE	POOR	✓		✓	✓	✓	✓
ONE PART			PVA	RESIN W / UNI BOND	LIQUID	15–60 MINS	YES	FAIR	✓	✓			✓	
		CEMENT		TENSOL / PVC / POLYSTYRENE	LIQUID	4 HOURS	LIGHT PRESSURE	POOR			✓	✓		
	CELLULOSE			BOSTIC / UHU	LIQUID	15 MINS	LIGHT PRESSURE	FAIR	✓					
TWO PART				CASCAMITE	POWDER	4–6 HOURS	YES	GOOD					✓	
TWO PART				CASCOPHEN	POWDER/LIQUID		YES	POOR						
TWO PART				AEROLITE	POWDER		YES	GOOD						
TWO PART				ARALDITE RAPID	LIQUID	10–20 MINS	YES							✓

USES

63

Glossary

Development

The unfolded shape of an object. This can be produced from the plan and elevation.

Elevation

An orthographic view (see **orthographic projection**) of the front or end of an object.

Fabricated

Built from separate pieces which are joined together.

Orthographic projection

A series of flat views of an object showing it exactly as it is in shape and size.

Perspective

A drawing system used to produce realistic views in which the lines converge to one or more vanishing points in the distance, creating the illusion of 3D.

Plan

An orthographic view (see **orthographic projection**) of an object from above.

Thermoplastic

A plastic that can be softened by heat.

TPI

Teeth per inch – the way in which the coarseness of a saw blade is described.

Vacuum forming

A method of forming a thermoplastic sheet by heating it until soft, then pumping the air out from the mould chamber of the machine, and sucking the plastic down onto a mould.